Star of the Air

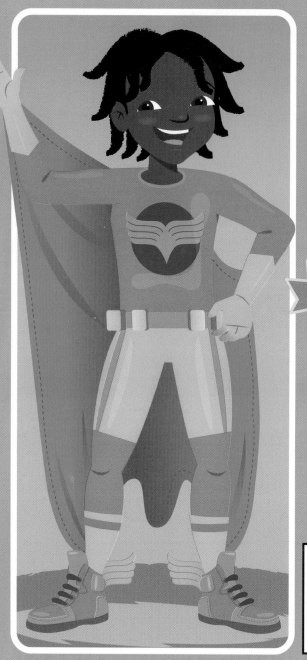

I am Marvin, Star of the Air.

Marvin helps to stop robbers.

Look! It is Robert the robber.

Robert the robber gets onto the silver ship.

Robert jumps back into his hot air balloon. The men ring Marvin. He is sure to help if he is near.

Can you help us, Marvin?

Ring! Ring!

Marvin **is** near.

I **can** help!

Zoom!

He aims a dart
at his target.

6

The dart hits the balloon!

Robert's hot air balloon starts to go down.

Help me and you can keep all the coins.

SSss!

The coins can go back to the silver ship.

8

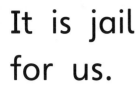

It is jail for us.

They zoom off to jail on surf scooters.

Jail for us!

Marvin, Star of the Air, zooms off too.

Zoom!